The First Day

PICTURES AND STORY BY

PELAGIE DOANE

PHILADELPHIA

J. B. Lippincott Company

NEW YORK

To all the children in this book

This is Gary during the week and his brother David and his sister Lynn.

This is Gary on Sunday

and his brother David

and his sister Lynn.

They are all going to Sunday School together.

"Today's my first day at Sunday School!"
"Why that's fine. That's fine," said Mr. O'Toole.

"Jeb and Suzanne are going to Sunday School with us today!"
"How nice. And how nice you look," answered Miss Gray.

"Hey wait, Jimmy. Wait for us. You, too, Mary Sue."
"I have some pennies to give. Did you bring some, too?"

Then up the steps they went, and along the hall.

Miss Mattie was there with a smile for them all.

And there were the rest of their friends: Molly and Penny
And Clyde and Billy, Conrad and Brucie and Jay and Kenny.

The older children left the young ones to go to their own classes.
They waved to them from the door.
"You'll have fun, we know," they said.
"We'll be back when Sunday School is over. Don't dare leave before."

The teacher gave them all their lesson folders
with colored pictures on the covers.
And they all looked at the pictures.
Gary's was the same as all the others.

"Who knows his memory verse?" they heard Miss Mattie say.
Gary didn't have one for this was his first day.

"Now the morning song we'll sing.
"Let your voices ring and ring."

Jesus wants me for his sunbeam
To shine for Him all day.
In every way, try to please Him
At home, at school, at play.

Miss Mattie played soft music as they marched to their seats.
Then she said, "Now we will pray."

They stood by their chairs and bowed their heads.
They folded their hands, and they began to say,

Lamb of God, I look to Thee;
Thou shalt my example be;
Thou art gentle, meek and mild;
Thou wast once a little child.

"Here's the basket.
Who will pass it?"
"Let's all put our pennies in.
One, two, three, four, five, six, seven ...."

Jimmy'd had a birthday. Wednesday he was five.
A penny for each year. One, two, three, four, five.

And now it's time to sing
Another little song.

Jesus loves me, this I know
For the Bible tells me so.
Little ones to Him belong;
They are weak and He is strong.

Then the teacher told how Jesus loved little children.
She told how he taught them to love one another.
She showed a picture of Jesus with children round him.
They all looked at the picture on their lesson cover.

Jesus loves little children, all the children of the world wherever they live, whatever their names. Jesus loves the little children of the world.

"Now we will color the pictures the best we are able.
Jeb get the crayons. Come, children, let's fix the table."

"Keep within the lines," the teacher said.
"Use the colors, yellow, blue and red,
Orange, lavender and pink.
This one's pretty, don't you think?"

Miss Mattie played some tunes. The children tried to guess their names,
And sing a little, too.
Gary liked this part and sang with the other children
All of the words he knew.

The bell rang.
The children sang.

Our Sunday School is over
And we are going home.
Good-bye. Good-bye.
Be always kind and good.

They said good-bye to Miss Mattie.
And they all marched through the doorway.

The older children were waiting for them as they said they would.
They waved to Miss Mattie and she said they'd been good.

And they all went skipping home.

in different directions.

But they'll all meet next Sunday,
In Sunday School together.

RECL

Date Due

NO 13 '64			
MY 13 '74			